# SCIENCE

The aim of this book is to help children
understand the basic elements of science
and encourage them to enjoy learning about
the world around us.

●

How To Be Top is divided into sections, each
dealing with a different scientific topic. The book
is packed with information, some helpful
illustrations and lots of exercises to test your child's
newly acquired knowledge. All the exercises
require short answers which can be checked with
the answers at the back of the book.

●

A knowledge of basic science is a vital part of
your child's education and life, but it is far less
popular with today's children than ever before.
How To Be Top aims to inspire children
and help them enjoy studying this
fascinating subject.

*Vicky Spawls*

# CONTENTS

This edition published for Independent Book Supplies Ltd in 2010
by Arcturus Publishing Limited

Copyright © Arcturus Publishing Limited, 26/27 Bickels Yard, 151–153 Bermondsey Street,
London SE1 3HA

ISBN: 978-1-84837-559-8
CH000644EN

Printed in India

Author: Vicky Spawls. Editor: Paula Field. Designer: Tania Field

# LIVING THINGS
## TEST 1

There are millions and millions of different kinds of living things in the world. **Some are very big like trees, whales and elephants** and **some are very small like ants, bacteria and viruses.** Not everything in the world is alive. For example, stones, water and cars are not alive.

*Non-living*　　　　　　*Living*　　　　　*Living*

The main difference between living things and non-living things is that living things can:

breathe　　grow and reproduce　　move about

sense things around them

they all need food to survive

1. From the list below write down the things that:

   **a.** animals can do　　**b.** a car can do　　**c.** a plant can do

   _____　　_____　　_____
   _____　　_____　　_____
   _____　　_____　　_____
   _____　　_____　　_____

   move from place to place　　breathe

   reproduce　　make their own food

   heal themselves when they get damaged

   grow　　　　eat food

2. Put the following things into two groups: **living** and **non-living**:

   elephant,　microwave oven,　stream,　bicycle, oak tree,　human being,　bottle,　train, bee,　cat,　fish,　glass

   **Living**　　　　　　　　**Non-living**

   _____　　　　　_____
   _____　　　　　_____
   _____　　　　　_____
   _____　　　　　_____
   _____　　　　　_____
   _____　　　　　_____

Now you know all about living and non-living things, award yourself a star in the box, left.

3

# THE FOOD CHAIN
## TEST 2

**All living things need food for energy and growth.**
Plants make their own food but animals can't. This means that animals have to get their food from elsewhere. Plants serve as food for most animals, even if they don't eat them directly. For example, a worm eats leaves and other bits of plants; the worm is eaten by a bird and the bird is eaten by a cat. Although the cat and the bird don't eat the plant themselves, they still depend on it to survive.

This is called a food chain. The food chain shows how food is passed from the leaf to the worm and then on to the bird.

**Animals that eat plants are called herbivores.**
**Animals that eat other animals are called carnivores.**
**Animals that eat plants and animals are called omnivores.**

**1.** Foxes eat rabbits; carrots are plants which make their own food; rabbits eat carrots.

**a.** Draw a food chain to show this information.

**b.** Which animal in this food chain is a herbivore?
_____

**c.** What would happen to the foxes if the rabbits died?
_____

**2.** What is the difference between an omnivore and a carnivore?
_____

**3.** Look at this list of living things. For each one say whether it is a plant, a herbivore or a carnivore:

**a.** grass     **b.** sheep     **c.** dog
_____ _____ _____

**d.** lion     **e.** deer     **f.** rosebush
_____ _____ _____

**4**

Once you have understood how a food chain works, award yourself a star in the box, right.

**Humans are animals**. There are millions of different types of animal in the world but they all have certain features in common. For example, all animals have to eat food because they can't make food in their own bodies, like plants can.

Humans (including you) are animals, and like all animals you need to eat food every day to stay alive. Food has three important functions in your body:

| to give you energy | to help you grow | to keep you healthy |
|---|---|---|

1. Why do all animals have to eat food?

   _____

2. Why don't plants have to eat food?

   _____

3. Almost all food is good for you, but some can be harmful if you eat too much. Look at this list of food and drink:

| Cola drink | Milk | Bread | Baked beans |
|---|---|---|---|
| Fruit | Potatoes | Chocolate | Chips |
| Eggs | Crisps | Beefburger | Vegetables |

a. Which of these is it good to have lots of every day?

   _____

b. Which should you have only very occasionally?

   _____

c. Which are very good for you, but you don't need them every day?

   _____

Now you know what you should and shouldn't eat, award yourself a star in the box, left.

5

Another feature common to animals is that they can all move around from place to place. However, they all have very different features depending on how and where they live – this is called adaptation.  For example:

**Fish are adapted to live in the sea.**
They have a tail and fins which allow them to swim and gills which allow them to get oxygen from the water so that they can breathe.

**Cats are adapted to live on land.**
They have legs which allow them to walk and run; claws to help them climb trees and catch prey; and lungs to breathe air.

1.  Link these features with the animal's activity:

    **1** fur          **a** walking and running
    **2** claws      **b** climbing trees
    **3** teeth       **c** flying
    **4** legs        **d** breathing air
    **5** gills        **e** breathing under water
    **6** wings     **f** swimming
    **7** lungs      **g** keeping warm
    **8** fins        **h** eating food

2.  Polar bears live on land in very cold, icy places and they eat fish. Choose five adaptations from the list above that polar bears have.

    _____

3.  Butterflies and birds all have wings.
    What does this tell you about how they move around ? _____

4.  Whales live in the sea but they have lungs, not gills.
    What does this tell you about how they breathe ?

    _____

5.  Bats have fur, wings, lungs and teeth. What does this tell you about how they live ?

    _____

**6**

When you can identify an animal's lifestyle by its adaptations, award yourself a star in the box, right.

**Blood** is a very important liquid that carries food and oxygen around your body. This food and oxygen is vital to organs, such as your brain and muscles. The blood is kept moving by a special pump called your **heart**, which is found in the middle of your chest and slightly to the left. Your heart is made of muscle and is about the size of your clenched fist.

When the heart muscle contracts (gets smaller) it pushes blood out of the heart and it travels to all parts of your body in tubes called arteries. When the heart muscle relaxes, blood flows back into it through tubes called veins.

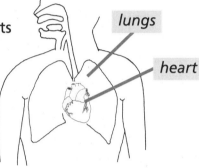

*lungs*

*heart*

Like other muscles and organs in your body, your heart needs to be looked after and there are a few things to remember:

| Do not smoke | Eat a balanced diet | Take regular exercise |

1. What happens when your heart contracts?

   _____

2. Match these words with their functions:

   **1** heart     **a** carries blood back to the heart

   **2** blood     **b** pumps blood around the body

   **3** artery     **c** carries food and oxygen around the body

   **4** vein     **d** carries blood away from the heart

3. How does food and oxygen travel around your body?

   _____

4. Which of the following are **good** for your heart and **bad** for your heart
   a. drinking lots of beer __ b. walking to the shops __
   c. eating fruit and vegetables __ d. smoking __
   e. eating cream cakes __ f. driving to the shops __
   g. 10 minutes skipping every day __

Every time your heart contracts, it is known as a **heartbeat**. You can feel this movement by putting your hand on your heart or by feeling the pulse on your neck or your wrist. By counting your pulse you can measure how many heartbeats you have each minute.

Your heart beats at different rates depending on what you are doing. Exercise makes your heart beat faster. This is because your muscles work very hard during exercise and they need lots of food and oxygen to keep them working. So your heart beats faster, pumping blood around the body so that it can deliver this food to where it is needed. When you stop exercising, your muscles begin to recover and don't need so much food and oxygen, so your heart slows down. Eventually it drops to its normal heartbeat rate, called the **resting rate**.

1. Jamie measured his pulse rate at three different times and found it was **70 beats per minute (bpm)**, **105 bpm** and **94 bpm**. From the above list, write down the pulse rates when Jamie was:

   a. exercising? _____

   b. resting? _____

   c. sitting down just after exercising? _____

2. What happens to your pulse rate when you exercise?
   _____

3. Which part of your body needs extra food and oxygen when you exercise?
   _____

4. Josh's pulse got faster when he exercised for five minutes. What is his pulse the measure of?
   _____

8

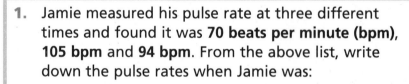

If you can take your pulse and understand what it means, award yourself a star in the box, right.

The air around us is made up of lots of different gases. **One particular gas is very important as we use it in our bodies to help us get energy from our food.** This gas is called oxygen.

When we breathe in, air is taken into our lungs and some of the oxygen in the air is absorbed into the blood which carries the oxygen around the body.

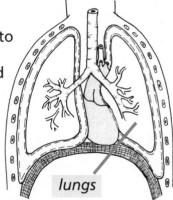

*lungs*

When we are relaxed we breathe at a rate of about 12 to 14 breaths per minute. But if we start to exercise our breathing rate speeds up and slows down when we stop.

1. Whereabouts in your body are your lungs found?

   a. chest       b. head       c. abdomen

2. What do we use oxygen for in our bodies?

   _____

3. How is oxygen carried to all parts of the body?

   _____

4. The graph right shows Susie's breathing rate when she is resting, then when she starts to exercise and when she stops exercising.

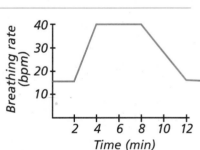

Breathing rate (bpm) vs Time (min)

   a. Between 0-2 minutes, was Susie resting or exercising? _____

   b. At what time did Susie start to exercise? _____

   c. What happened to her breathing rate when she was exercising? _____

   d. What happened to Susie's breathing rate after she stopped exercising? _____

   e. How long did it take for her breathing rate to get back to normal? _____

Once you understand how we breathe, award yourself a star in the box, left.

9

# THE SKELETON
## TEST 8

The bones inside your body are joined together to make your **skeleton**. There are over 200 bones in your skeleton. Some of them, such as those in your ear, are very small; while others, like those in your arms and legs, are quite large.

Your skeleton does three main jobs:

**It supports your body and stops you from flopping over.**

**It helps you to move.**

**It protects some of your important organs. For example, the skull protects your brain and your ribs protect your lungs.**

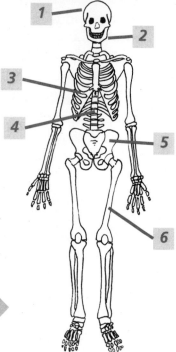

1. Which label on the above skeleton points to:

   **a.** skull ___  **b.** ribs ___  **c.** backbone ___
   **d.** jaw ___  **e.** pelvis ___  **f.** thighbone ___

2. Which of the bones labelled would be moving when:

   **a.** You talk  **b.** You walk  **c.** You breathe in deeply?

3. Not all animals have skeletons. Which of the following animals don't have skeletons?

   **a.** fish ___  **b.** worm ___  **c.** slug ___
   **d.** rabbit ___  **e.** frog ___  **f.** jellyfish ___

4. Complete this passage:
   The skull and the ribs are made of **b** _____ and form part of the **s** _____ . The **s** _____ is found in the head where it protects the **b** _____ .
   The **r** _____ are found in the **c** _____ , where they protect the **h** _____ and **l** _____ .

10

When you understand what your skeleton does, award yourself a star in the box, right.

Joints connect bones together. They allow your body to move around and there are two main types:

A hinge joint, such as your knee. The joint is behind your knee cap and allows you to move your lower leg backwards and forwards, but not side to side.

A ball and socket joint, such as your shoulder joint. This joint alllows you to move your arm from side to side as well as backwards and forwards.

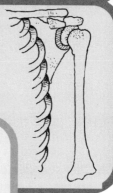

Muscles are attached to your bones and allow you to move. Muscles work in pairs by contracting (getting shorter). When a muscle contracts it pulls on the bone it is attached to and makes it move. For example, when your biceps muscle contracts, your arm moves up and when its pair, the triceps, contracts, your arm moves down.

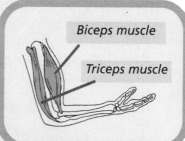

Biceps muscle

Triceps muscle

1. What does a joint do?

2. Name one other hinge joint and one other ball and socket joint.

3. What does contracting mean?

4. What happens when the biceps muscle in your arm contracts?

Once you know all about joints and muscles, award yourself a star in the box, left.

11

Like many other animals humans have teeth to help them eat. **Teeth are part of your skeleton and they are fixed into your jaw bone.** As a young child you will have a total of 20 teeth, which are called milk teeth. These will gradually fall out and will be replaced by new ones.

You have three different types of tooth:

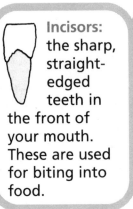

**Incisors:** the sharp, straight-edged teeth in the front of your mouth. These are used for biting into food.

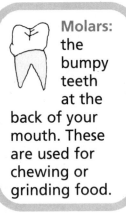

**Molars:** the bumpy teeth at the back of your mouth. These are used for chewing or grinding food.

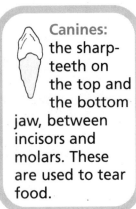

**Canines:** the sharp-teeth on the top and the bottom jaw, between incisors and molars. These are used to tear food.

**Teeth are very hard, but they can be destroyed by acid.** Acid is produced by tiny germs called bacteria that live in your mouth and feed on the sugar in your food. This layer of bacteria is called **plaque**. **It is important to brush and floss your teeth every day, to remove the plaque.**

1. Which types of teeth do you use for:

   a. biting?     b. chewing?     c. tearing?

2. What is plaque?

   _____

3. Which of the following could be bad for your teeth?

   a. apple juice ___  b. sweets ___  c. carrots ___
   d. potatoes ___  e. apples ___  f. crisps ___
   g. cola drink ___  h. chocolate ___

4. Why must you clean your teeth regularly?

   _____

5. How many milk teeth does a young child have?

   _____

Now you know what your different teeth do, award yourself a star in the box, right.

**Like all living things** humans reproduce. This means they **produce baby humans that grow up into adult humans**.

The type of reproduction found in humans is called sexual reproduction because it involves **two parents, one male and one female**. When a man and a woman make love, special cells called sperm are passed from the man to the woman, inside her body.

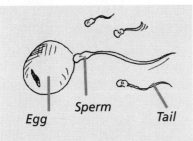

Egg    Sperm    Tail

Sometimes one of the **sperm cells** finds its way to another **special cell called an egg** in the woman's body, and the two cells join together. This is called fertilization.

*Sperm cells have a tail so that they can swim to the egg.*

When the egg and the sperm join together inside the female's body we call it **internal fertilization**. Many other animals produce babies in the same way. However, some animals use **external fertilization**. For example, when fish mate, they both release their sex cells directly into the water. The sperm from the male then swims through the water to join the female's egg. Many of the sperm don't make it and die.

1. What do we call the sex cells produced by:

   **a.** a man?                    **b.** a woman?

   _____          _____

2. How are sperm cells designed for their job?

   _____

3. What does fertilization mean?

   _____

4. Fish produce many more sex cells than humans. Why do you think this is?

   _____

5. What does reproduction mean?

   _____

When you know how an egg is fertilized, award yourself a star in the box, left.

In a woman, once the egg and the sperm have joined together, the **fertilized egg** grows into a baby in a special place called the **uterus** or **womb**. While the baby is growing, the woman is pregnant. The baby takes nine months to grow inside its mother's body before it is ready to be born. This is called the **gestation period**. The gestation period lasts for a different length of time in different mammals.

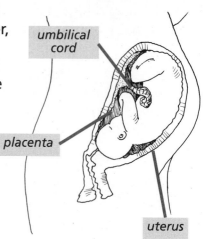

umbilical cord

placenta

uterus

While the baby is inside its mother's uterus it cannot feed itself or breathe for itself. Instead it gets all the food and oxygen it needs from its mother. Inside her body is a special organ called the **placenta**. The mother's and the baby's blood travels through the placenta and the baby's blood absorbs the things it needs to stay alive and grow through the umbilical cord. **This happens in all mammals.**

1. What does gestation period mean?

   _____

2. Which of the following mammals do you think has the longest gestation period?

   **a.** elephant  **b.** rabbit  **c.** human  **d.** dog

3. Where in the mother's body does the baby grow?

   **a.** stomach  **b.** liver  **c.** uterus

4. While a woman is pregnant how does the baby get the food and oxygen it needs to grow?

   _____

5. Why do you think it is important for a pregnant woman to eat a good, balanced diet?

   _____

Once you have correctly completed this page, award yourself a star in the box, right.

**We all start life as a single fertilized egg cell and eventually grow up into an adult person.**

We spend the first nine months of our lives growing from a single cell into a baby inside our mother's uterus.

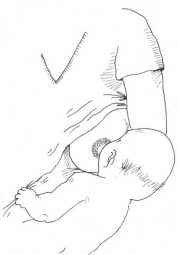

**In the first few months of a baby's life, the mother feeds it with milk made specially for the baby in her breasts.** All mammals produce milk for their babies. The milk contains all the important nutrients that the baby needs to grow and prevent it getting ill.

When we are born we are completely helpless, and our parents have to do everything for us. They have to feed us, clean us, keep us warm and protect us. It is also very important that we are loved, talked to and taught. This helps to develop our minds as well as our bodies.

Other animals, such as birds, also look after their babies by feeding, protecting and keeping them warm.

1. Give two reasons why mother's milk is the best thing for newborn babies?

   _____

2. Only mammals feed their babies with milk. Which of these animals provide milk for their babies?

   **a.** fish __    **b.** humans __    **c.** elephants __    **d.** birds __

3. Why do you think it is important for parents to talk to their babies?

   _____

4. A newborn baby is completely helpless. List three ways in which adults must look after a baby?

   _____

Now you know how to look after a newborn baby, award yourself a star in the box left.

15

# GROWTH AND DEVELOPMENT
## TEST 14

**From our birth to the age of 18 years** we are continually **growing and getting bigger** and our **bodies and minds are changing and developing**. Many changes take place during this time.

The first three years of our life after we are born is called our infancy. **This is when we learn to walk and talk.**

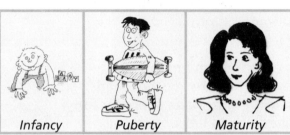

Infancy     Puberty     Maturity

Between the ages of 12 years and 15 years we go through another important stage called puberty. (In some people puberty can occur earlier than 12 and later than 15). This is when our **bodies start to develop sexually** so that girls start to produce eggs and boys start to produce sperm.

By the time we reach 18 years, our bodies are **fully grown**, and we are said to have reached maturity; but our minds may continue to develop for many years.

---

1. Link these important stages in our lives with the correct ages.

   | 1. Infancy | a. 12 – 15 years |
   | 2. Puberty | b. 18 years |
   | 3. Maturity | c. 0 – 3 years |

2. At what age do girls and boys start to develop sexually?

   _____

3. Link the following words with their correct meaning.

   | 1. Reproduction | a. a gradual change in the body |
   | 2. Growth | b. producing new human beings |
   | 3. Development | c. a gradual increase in size. |

---

**16**

When you understand about puberty and adulthood, award yourself a star in the box, right.

Plants have **roots**, **stems** and sometimes **flowers**.

The **roots are found in the soil**. They branch and spread out to reach as much of the soil as they can. The roots have two functions. They hold the plant down in the soil and they absorb water and minerals from the soil, which the plant needs to live.

The **flowers** have just one function. **Their job is to produce baby plants through sexual reproduction**.

The **stem links the other organs of the plant together**. It holds the leaves up high so that they can get lots of sunlight and carbon dioxide to make food; it also holds the flowers up which helps them to reproduce; and the stem also passes water and minerals from the roots to the leaves and flowers, and food from the leaves down to the roots.

1. Look at the picture of the plant Which label points to:

   a. the roots?____    b. a leaf?____

   c. the stem?____    d. a flower?____

2. Which labelled part:

   a. makes food for the plant? ____
   b. transports food and water? through the plant? ____
   c. carries out reproduction? ____
   d. absorbs water from the soil? ____

3. What are the two main functions of the roots?

   _____

4. Why is the stem of a plant so important?

   _____

5. What is the job of a flower?
   a. to look nice  ____    b. to reproduce  ____
   c. to make food  ____

**Plants are living things because they can grow and reproduce.** Unlike animals they do not need to eat food because they can make their own. They do this through a process known as **photosynthesis**.

**Photosynthesis happens in the leaves of the plant.**
The leaf needs three things to make food:

| **Water** which it gets from the soil. | A gas called **carbon dioxide** which it gets from the air. | **Light energy** which it gets from the sun. |
|---|---|---|

For photosynthesis the plant needs to be quite warm. The food that is made in the leaf by photosynthesis is then used to give the plant energy and to help it grow and reproduce.

carbon dioxide from the air

light energy from the sun

water from the soil

---

1. What is photosynthesis?

   _____

2. Name 3 things a plant needs for photosynthesis.

   _____

3. Why do plants grow faster in the summer than in the winter?

   _____

4. Mr Patel left a cardboard box on his lawn for two weeks. When he lifted it up, he found that the grass underneath was dead. Explain why this happened.

   _____

5. During photosynthesis, plants make oxygen as well as food. We can write the process of photosynthesis like a sum. Complete this:

   **Carbon Dioxide + (a) _____ + (b) _____**

   **= (c) _____ + Oxygen**

---

Once you have learnt how plants make food, award yourself a star in the box, right.

**Like all living things plants are able to reproduce.**
To carry out sexual reproduction, plants have to make
special sex cells. The male sex cells are called **pollen**;
and the female sex cell is the **egg**. These are made
inside the flower.

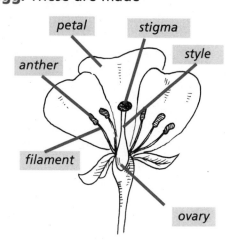

The male part of the flower is
called the **stamen**. It is made
up of the **anther**, which is
where the pollen grains are
made, and is held up by a
stalk called the **filament**.

The female part of the flower
is called the **carpel**. It is made
up of the **style, stigma** and
the **ovary**, where the eggs are
made. In order for the plants
to reproduce, the male pollen
grains have to be moved or transferred from an anther
to a carpel, usually of a different flower.

---

**1.** Look at these flower parts

| anther | ovary | stigma |
| filament | style | petals |

**a.** Which of these parts makes up the stamen?

_____

**b.** What is the name of the female part of the flower?

_____

**c.** Where are eggs made?

_____

**d.** Where are pollen grains made?

_____

---

When you can identify all the parts of a plant,
award yourself a star in the box, left.

19

# POLLINATION
# TEST 18

When pollen is transferred from the male part a flower to the female part of another flower, it is called **pollination.**

Pollination can happen in two ways. Some plants have brightly coloured petals, which attract insects such as bees to the flower. The pollen from one flower sticks to the bee's body, and then gets rubbed off onto the stigma of another flower, when the bee visits it.

Other flowers have small plain petals and are not attractive to insects. With these kinds of plants, the anthers and the stigma hang outside. When the wind blows it picks up pollen from one flower and carries it to another flower.

*Insect pollination*

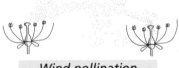

*Wind pollination*

During pollination, pollen lands on the stigma of a flower. The pollen grain then grows down through the style into the ovary of the flower. Here it joins with an egg inside the ovary. This is called **fertilization**.

1. What does the word pollination mean?
   _____

2. Explain the difference between insect pollination and wind pollination
   _____

3. Roses have brightly coloured petals and grass flowers have dull green petals. What does this tell us about how they transfer pollen?
   _____

4. During pollination, where on the plant does the pollen land?
   _____

  Once you have understood how flowers are pollinated, award yourself a star in the box, right.

After fertilization the **egg grows into a seed** that contains a **tiny baby plant** and a **food store**.

When the seeds have grown to a certain size they have to leave the plant they are growing on, and spread out to grow on their own. The spreading out of seeds is called **dispersal**. It is important for plants to disperse their seeds. If not, the baby plants that grow from the seeds would not get enough sunlight and water, as the parent plant would get it all. This means that the baby plant would not grow properly.

Plants use different ways of dispersing their seeds. For example, the **seeds of a peach grow inside a juicy fruit**. Animals such as humans, pick the peach and eat it, and then throw away the seed from the middle.

juicy fruit

seed

feathery parachute

seed

**Dandelion seeds grow with a feathery parachute around them**. The wind blows the seeds away from the parent plant. When the seed has been dispersed and lands on the ground it may start to grow.

1. What would you find inside a seed?

_____

2. What does seed dispersal mean?

_____

3. Sycamore trees produce seeds with little wing-like parts attached to them, but blackberries produce seeds inside a juicy fruit. How do you think sycamore seeds and blackberry seeds are dispersed?

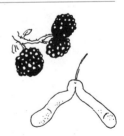

_____

4. What would happen to the seeds if they were not dispersed and started growing right under the parent plant?

_____

If all your answers are correct, award yourself a star in the box, left.

21

**When the baby plant starts to grow from the seed** we say that the **seed is germinating**. For germination a seed needs **water, oxygen** and **warmth**. The baby plant uses up the food store in the seed and starts to grow. First it grows tiny roots down into the soil, and then a stem with leaves on it grows up towards the light.

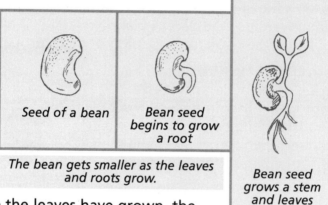

Seed of a bean

Bean seed begins to grow a root

The bean gets smaller as the leaves and roots grow.

Bean seed grows a stem and leaves

Once the leaves have grown, the baby plant is able to **photosynthesize** and can make its own food.

1. What does the word germinate mean?

2. Name three things that a seed needs to germinate.

3. Why will seeds not germinate in a refrigerator?

4. Can you think of a reason why

   **a.** the root of a baby plant grows downwards into the soil

   **but**

   **b.** the stem and leaves grow upwards?

Once you have learnt all about germination, award yourself a star in the box, right.

Electricity is a type of energy that flows through certain materials. Materials that allow electricity to flow through them are called conductors.

Metals are good conductors

but most other materials are insulators because they don't allow electricity to flow through them.

There are **two main sources of electricity** in our homes. Some things use **electricity from sockets**, which comes through underground wires from enormous power stations; while others use **batteries** which make electricity from chemicals reacting together.

Some things in **nature also produce electricity**. For example, lightning is caused by massive bolts of electricity from the clouds, and we use the electricity in our nerves to send messages around our bodies.

1. Is electricity a type of:

   **a.** force?__   **b.** energy?__   **c.** chemical reaction?__

2. Look at this list of things that use electricity in the home. Which ones use batteries and which ones use electricity from sockets?

   **a.** pocket calculator ___   **e.** bedside lamp ___
   **b.** computer ___   **f.** hand torch ___
   **c.** refrigerator ___   **g.** personal stereo ___
   **d.** vacuum cleaner ___

3. Write down five things that might be found in a kitchen that use electricity.

   _____

Now you know what uses electricity and what uses batteries, award yourself a star in the box, left.

23

Metal is a **conductor of electricity**. In our homes we use metal wires to carry electricity into and out of electrical appliances such as washing machines, radios and lights.

Metal is also a good **conductor of heat** and we use metals for making things like radiators and saucepans when we want heat to pass through them easily.

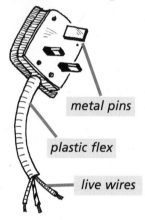

metal pins

plastic flex

live wires

However, although electricity and heat are very useful, they can also be very dangerous. If we touched a live metal wire (one carrying electricity), we would get an electric shock. So the electric wires in our homes are covered in plastic as plastic is a good **electrical insulator**.

When a saucepan has been used for cooking, the handle would get very hot if it was made of metal and we would burn ourselves trying to pick it up. So the handle is usually made of wood or plastic. Wood and plastic do not conduct heat as they are good **heat insulators**.

1.  Divide these things into four groups –
    **heat conductors, heat insulators, electrical conductors** and **electrical insulators**:

    metal saucepan   wooden stick   aluminium
    paper   plastic cup   string   silver bracelet
    china plate   copper wire   iron   gold

    **Heat conductors** _____
    **Heat insulators** _____
    **Electrical conductors** _____
    **Electrical insulators** _____

2.  What do we mean when we say something is:
    **a.** a good conductor of heat?
    **b.** a good insulator of electricity?
    _____

Once you have learnt about conductors and insulators, award yourself a star in the box, right.

Even though we don't always realise it, **we are surrounded by forces all the time**. Some examples of forces include:

| Gravity | Elastic | Friction | Upthrust |
|---------|---------|----------|----------|
| pulls everything down towards the earth | such as when you stretch a rubber band | makes it hard to rub two rough surfaces together | force of water that stops boats from sinking |

A **force** can be described as a push or a pull. When forces act on an object, they can make the object:

**move faster**      **slow down**

**change its shape**      **change direction**

However, if two forces act on an object in **opposite directions**, they may balance out, so nothing happens. In this picture, gravity pulls down on the girl, but the chair is pushing up so she doesn't move. Gravity is pulling down on the book, but friction between the book and the girl's hands balances the gravity, so the book doesn't move.

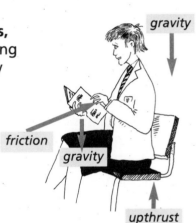

gravity

friction

gravity

upthrust

1. Which two words can be used to describe a force?

    _____    _____

2. Look at this boat on the water.

    a. Name the two forces acting on the boat.

    _____    _____

    b. Why doesn't the boat move up or down?

    _____

    c. What would happen if gravity became greater than the upthrust?

    _____

Now you know all about forces, award yourself a star in the box, left.

 25

**Magnetism is a type of force.** If a magnet is placed close to some iron pins and some wooden matches, the pins will be pulled towards the magnet and will stick to it. However, the wooden matches will not move. This is because magnetism attracts only specific metals and nothing else.

> **Anything made out of iron, steel, cobalt or nickel can be attracted to a magnet.**

The two ends of a magnet are called the **poles**. One is called the **north pole** and the other the **south pole**.

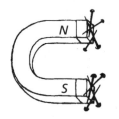

*Iron pins will be attracted to either end of a magnet, but the matchsticks will be unaffected.*

However, when we put two magnets together, they may be attracted to each other or they may be pushed away (repelled). **While a north pole and a south pole attract each other, two north or two south poles will repel each other.**

1. Is magnetism a type of:

   **a.** energy?__   **b.** force?__   **c.** electricity?__

2. Simon has dropped steel keys and some copper coins behind the sofa. Can he get them both out using a magnet on a string?

   _____

3. Name four types of metal that magnets attract.

   _____

4.

   **a.** Explain what will happen to the magnets (above).

   _____

   **b.** What will happen if one of the magnets is turned round the opposite way?

   _____

Now you know what is and isn't magnetic, award yourself a star in the box, right.

**Light is a type of energy that moves from one place to another.** Some things, such as the sun or a light bulb, make their own light. They are called light sources and we can see them because light from them travels into our eyes.

**Most objects don't make their own light,** but we can still see them because light from a light source hits the object and bounces off into our eyes.

**Light travels in straight lines.** This is why we see shadows. If you stand between a lamp and a wall, a dark patch (your shadow) forms on the wall where the light can't reach – because light can't travel through your body.

**Light travels fastest through empty space**, but it also moves through most gases, some liquids and a few solids.

*If the torch is moved further away from the object, the shadow will become smaller.*

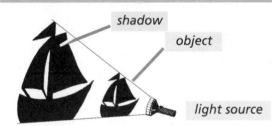

shadow

object

light source

1. Is light a type of:

   **a.** force?__   **b.** electricity ?__   **c.** energy ?__

2. Which of these objects is a light source?

   **a.** a flame __   **b.** a book __   **c.** a car headlamp __
   **d.** a television __   **e.** a radio __   **f.** the sun __

3. Complete this sentence with the correct statement from below. We can see a ball because:

   **a.** light from our eyes goes to the ball
   **b.** a ball is a light source
   **c.** light reflects off the ball and into our eyes

   _____

4. Why can we see through a glass window, but not through a brick wall?

   _____

Once you understand how light works,
award yourself a star in the box, left.

27

If you pluck a string on a guitar, two things happen. You can **see** the string moving back and forth very quickly; we say that **the string is vibrating**.

You also **hear** a sound. **This is because the vibration of the string makes the air particles around it vibrate.** The vibrations spread out through the air and into your ear where you '**hear**' it. Unlike light, sounds can be made by all sorts of things, when they move and cause vibrations.

**Sound vibrations can travel through all the things around us, whether solids, liquids or gases.** As long as an object is made of particles (as every object is) the particles can vibrate back and forth. Sound travels fastest through solids and slowest through gases.

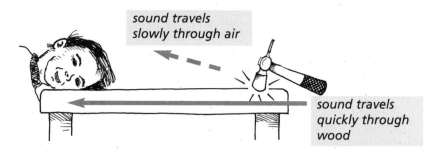

*sound travels slowly through air*

*sound travels quickly through wood*

1. What do we mean when we say that something is vibrating?

   _____

2. How does the sound travel from a drum into your ears?

   _____

3. Put these three objects in order, according to how fast sound travels through them, from the slowest to the fastest:

   a. a metal pipe ___
   b. water in a swimming pool ___
   c. air ___

4. If an astronaut on the moon dropped a rock, why couldn't she hear it hit the surface?

   _____

**28**

Everything around us can be described as either a solid, a liquid or a gas. For example the air is a gas; water is a liquid; and tables and paper are solids.

The steam from a kettle is a gas

Cooking oil is a liquid

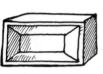

A brick is a solid

Some things, such as water, can change easily from solid to liquid, from liquid to gas and back again.

| Solid water is called ice | Liquid water is just called water | Water as a gas is called steam or water vapour. |
|---|---|---|

The main difference between solids, liquids and gases is the amount of heat energy they have. If you heat a lump of ice it turns into water; and if you heat water in a saucepan it turns into steam. On the other hand, water placed in a freezer will lose heat and turn to ice.

1. Divide these things into solids, liquids and gases.

   water vapour    orange juice
   oxygen    wood    blood    glass
   ice    carbon dioxide

   Solids          Liquids          Gases
   _____       _____        _____

2. What happens to steam when it cools down?

   _____

3. Link these words to their meanings:

   1. melting        a. changing from a liquid to a gas

   2. freezing       b. changing from a solid to a liquid

   3. evaporating    c. changing from a liquid to a solid

Now you know the difference between solids, liquids and gases, award yourself a star in the box, left.

29

The things around us are made up of different **materials.** For example, **some things are made of wood, some are made of metal and others are made of plastic, glass, paper, cloth** and so on.

**Different materials are used because of their different properties.** There are many different properties which include **hardness, softness, strength or flexibility,** and you would choose your material according to what you needed your object for.

For example, **aluminium and iron are both types of metal.** They are both very hard and strong, but they also have other very different properties and are used for different things. Aluminium is used for making aeroplanes, because it is much lighter than iron. **Cars are made out of iron because it is stronger than aluminium.**

**1.** Match these materials with their properties

| Materials | Properties |
|---|---|
| Wood | Brittle |
| Polythene | Hard |
| Glass | Strong |
| Metal | Flexible |
| Cloth | Waterproof |

**2.** Link these properties with their meanings

1. flexible   a. light passes through it
2. magnetic   b. does not break easily
3. strong   c. can be bent easily
4. brittle   d. easy to break or snap
5. transparent   e. attracted to magnets

**3.** Why do cars use liquid petrol and not solid coal as fuel? Choose one of the following statements:

a. Liquids weigh less than solids
b. Liquids are cheaper than solids
c. Liquids flow and solids do not

Now you know how to choose the right material, award yourself a star in the box, right.

**TEST 1**
1a. breathe, move from place to place, reproduce, grow, eat food   1b. none of these   1c. breathe, reproduce, make their own food, heal themselves when they get damaged, grow
2. **Living** – elephant, oak tree, human being, bee, cat, fish
**Non-living** – microwave oven, bicycle, bottle, train, stream, glass

**TEST 2**
1a.

1b. rabbit   1c. they would have no food
2. **omnivores** eat animals and plants; **carnivores** eat only animals.   3a. plant
3b. herbivore   3c. carnivore   3d. carnivore
3e. herbivore   3f. plant

**TEST 3**
1. To stay alive; to give energy; to help them grow; to keep healthy   2. They can make their own.   3a. fruit, vegetables, milk   3b. cola drink, chocolate, chips, beefburger, crisps   3c. bread, eggs, baked beans, potatoes

**TEST 4**
1. 1 - g; 2 - b; 3 - h; 4 - a; 5 - e; 6 - c; 7 - d; 8-f   2. fur, teeth, legs, lungs, claws
3. They fly   4. They breathe air.
5. They keep warm, they fly, they breathe air and they eat food

**TEST 5**
1. It pushes blood out of the heart and around the body.   2. 1 - b; 2 - c; 3 - d; 4 - a
3. Blood carries it around
4. **Good** – b, c and g   **Bad** – a, d, e and f

**TEST 6**
1. a. 105bpm; b. 70bpm; c. 94bpm
2. It gets faster   3. Your muscles
4. His heart beat

**TEST 7**
1. chest   2. To help us get energy from food.   3. In our blood   4a. resting;
4b. 2 minutes; 4c. it went up;
4d. it went down; e. 4 minutes

**TEST 8**
1. a - 1; b - 3; c - 4; d - 2; e - 5; f - 6
2. a -jaw; b - thighbone and pelvis; c - ribs
3. worm, slug and jellyfish   4. The skull and ribs are made of **bone** and form part of the **skeleton**. The **skull** is found in the head where it protects the **brain**. The **ribs** are found in the **chest**, where they protect the **heart** and **lungs**.

**TEST 9**
1. A joint connects bones together and allows you to move around.   2. **hinge joint** – elbow; **ball and socket joint** – hip
3. getting shorter   4. your arm moves up

**TEST 10**
1. a-incisors; b-molars; c-canines
2. A layer of bacteria   3. b-sweets, g-cola drink; h-chocolate   4. To remove the plaque   5. 20

**TEST 11**
1. a - sperm; b - egg   2. They have tails to help them swim   3. An egg and a sperm have joined together   4. Because most of them die   5. Producing babies

**TEST 12**
1. The amount of time a baby spends developing inside its mother's body before it is ready to be born.   2. a. an elephant – 22 months   3. c. uterus   4. From the mother's blood through the placenta
5. To provide the baby with all the nutrients it needs to grow, and to stay healthy herself

**TEST 13**
1. It provides them with food for growth and protects them from illness.
2. b-humans; c-elephants
3. So that they learn to talk and are able to communicate with others.
4. Feed them, clean them, keep them warm and protect them.

**TEST 14**
1. 1 - c; 2 - a; 3 - b   2. 12 to 15 years
3. 1 - b; 2 - c; 3 - a

**TEST 15**
1. a - 4; b - 2; c - 3; d - 1   2. a - 2; b - 3; c - 1; d - 4   3. Holds plant down in soil and absorbs water and minerals from the soil.
4. It links all the organs of the plant together; it holds up the leaves and flowers and it passes water and minerals to the parts of the plant that needs them.
5. b. to reproduce

# ANSWERS

## TEST 16
1. The process by which plants make food
2. Water, carbon dioxide and light
3. There is more sunlight and it is warmer
4. The grass got no light
5. a - water; b - light; c - food

## TEST 17
1. a-anther and filament; b - carpel;
c - ovary; d - anther

## TEST 18
1. The transfer of pollen from the male part of a flower to the female part of another flower   2. **Insect pollination** – the pollen is carried by insects, such as bees. **Wind pollination** – the pollen is carried by the wind.   3. Roses are insect pollinated; Grass is wind pollinated   4. Pollen lands on the stigma

## TEST 19
1. Tiny baby plant and food store
2. Spreading out the seeds   3. Sycamore seeds are dispersed by the wind. Blackberries are dispersed by insects or birds (and other animals)   4. They would not get enough food or light and would die.

## TEST 20
1. When a seed grows into a baby plant
2. Water, warmth and oxygen   3. It is too cold   4. a - to find water.  b - to reach the light

## TEST 21
1. b - a type of energy
2. **Batteries** – a, f and g.  **Sockets** – b, c, d and e   3. Microwave oven, cooker, kettle, washing machine, tumble dryer, dishwasher, iron, radio, food processor, toaster etc

## TEST 22
1. **Heat conductors** – aluminium, copper wire, metal saucepan, iron, gold
**Heat insulators** – plastic cup, wooden stick, string, paper
**Electrical conductors** – metal saucepan, copper wire, silver bracelet
**Electrical insulators** – wooden stick, plastic cup, china plate
2a. It allows heat to pass through it
2b. It does not allow electricity to pass through it

## TEST 23
1. a push or a pull
2a. gravity and upthrust   2b. the forces are balanced   2c. the boat would sink

## TEST 24
1. b - a type of force   2. No, he can get

the steel keys only. Copper is not attracted to magnets   3. iron, cobalt, nickel and steel   4a. they will repel
4b. they will attract

## TEST 25
1. c - a type of energy   2. a, c, d and f
3. statement c   4. glass is transparent so light travels through it, but bricks are not and light cannot get through.

## TEST 26
1. It is moving back and forth   2. By air particles vibrating   3. c - air; b - water; a - metal pipe   4. Because there is no air and therefore no particles to carry the sound.

## TEST 27
1. **Solids** – wood, glass, ice
**Liquids** – orange juice, blood
**Gases** – oxygen, water vapour, carbon dioxide   2. It turns back into a liquid
3. 1 - b; 2 - c; 3 - a

## TEST 28
1. **Wood** – hard and strong
**Polythene** – flexible and waterproof
**Glass** – brittle, hard and waterproof
**Metal** – hard, strong and waterproof
**Cloth** – flexible
2. 1 - c; 2 - e; 3 - b; 4 - d; 5 - a
3. c - liquids flow and solids do not